Fen Fixes Her Circuit

Fixing the Problem

Sadie Silva

Published in 2018 by The Rosen Publishing Group, Inc.
29 East 21st Street, New York, NY 10010

Copyright © 2018 by The Rosen Publishing Group, Inc.

All rights reserved. No part of this book may be
reproduced in any form without permission in writing
from the publisher, except by a reviewer.

Book Design: Jennifer Ryder-Talbot
Editor: Caitie McAneney

All illustrations by Contentra Technologies

Library of Congress Cataloging-in-Publication Data

Names: Silva, Sadie.
Title: Fen fixes her circuit: fixing the problem / Sadie Silva.
Description: New York : Rosen Classroom, 2018. | Series: Computer Kids: Powered by
Computational Thinking | Includes glossary and index.
Identifiers: LCCN ISBN 9781538353097 (pbk.) | ISBN 9781538323953 (library bound) |
ISBN 9781538355541 (6 pack) | ISBN 9781508137443 (ebook)
Subjects: LCSH: Electricity--Juvenile fiction.
Classification: LCC PZ7.S553 Fe 2018 | DDC [E]--dc23

Manufactured in the United States of America

CPSIA Compliance Information: Batch #WS18RC: For Further Information contact Rosen Publishing, New York, New York at 1-800-237-9932

Table of Contents

Fen's Circuit	4
What Kind of Circuit Is This?	7
Identifying Circuit Parts	8
Fen's Problem	10
Fen Checks the Battery	13
Fen Checks the Wires	14
Fen Checks the Bulb	16
One Last Thing	19
Fen Finds the Problem!	20
Fen's Solution	22
Glossary	23
Index	24

Fen's Circuit

Fen's mom is an electrical **engineer**. She has worked on all kinds of electrical systems, from those in buildings to robots to computers. Fen wants to learn how electricity works. Fen's mom buys her a circuit kit for her birthday. "Circuit kits are a great start when you're learning about how electricity works," her mom says.

Fen reads about circuits before she gets started. She learns that circuits are like electricity highways. They allow a power source, such as a battery, to power a device. Fen learns that the power lines outside her house carry electricity that powers her lights, TV, and laptop. When she turns on a light switch, electricity is able to flow to the light and power it.

What Kind of Circuit Is This?

Fen wants to learn more about the diffcrent kinds of circuits people use. Her mom says that there are two main kinds of circuits—series and parallel.

Fen's mom says that in series circuits, the whole **current** flows through every part of the circuit. If there is a circuit with multiple bulbs, like Christmas lights, this can be a problem. If one bulb blows out, then all of the lights turn off because the current is **disrupted**. In parallel circuits, the current is divided between branches, with only part of the current going through each branch. If one light bulb blows out in this kind of circuit, the other lights keep shining. Fen looks at her circuit. It is a series circuit!

Identifying Circuit Parts

Fen takes the parts out of her circuit kit. She wants to learn what each part does. There are only a few parts.

Fen looks at the light bulb that is included. This is the device that has to be powered by the battery. The battery is the power source. It has a little bump on one side. Fen's mom says that side of the battery is the positive side and the other side is the negative side. There are wires included that will connect the parts and create a pathway for electricity. The last part is the switch. It has an arm that goes up and down. It will let Fen turn the light on and off.

Fen's Problem

Fen's mom helps her connect the parts of her circuit. She uses little clips on the end of the wires to connect parts. First, she connects the positive side of the battery to the light bulb. Then, she connects the light bulb to the switch. Lastly, she connects the switch to the negative side of the battery.

Fen finishes her circuit! However, the light bulb doesn't light up. What could have gone wrong? Fen's mom says, "Sometimes things don't work the way you want them to the first time. You have to find the problem and fix it." Fen doesn't know where to start looking for the problem. Her mom says to go through each of the parts and check them one by one.

Fen Checks the Battery

Fen starts looking for the problem by checking the battery. This is the power source for the whole circuit. That means that if it doesn't work, then the whole circuit won't work.

Fen **researches** batteries. She learns that batteries are **containers** for energy. They store chemicals. When you use a battery, the chemical energy is **transformed** into electricity. Fen already knows about the negative and positive sides of the battery. Batteries work when there is an electrical difference between the two sides. If the battery is dead, then the battery won't have a **chemical reaction** and it won't work. Fen checks her battery in another device. It works in the new device. The problem must be something else!

Fen Checks the Wires

Next, Fen decides to check the wires on her circuit. She learns that wires have metal inside of them that is a **conductor**. The metal part is made of copper. It is a great conductor, and it allows electricity to flow through it. The wire is covered in a **material** that **insulates** it. Fen's mom says this keeps her from getting a shock when touching wires.

Fen checks the connections of the wires to the objects in the kit. Are all of the clips touching the correct parts of the objects? She finds out that her wires are connected correctly. The problem doesn't have to do with the wires. Fen keeps looking to find the source of her problem.

Fen Checks the Bulb

Fen checks the light bulb next. She wonders if this is the source of the problem. She realizes that she doesn't know how light bulbs actually work.

Fen looks up a **diagram** of a light bulb. There are three basic parts. There is a metal base, which conducts electricity. This is connected to a filament, which is a thin metal wire. It is made of a metal that heats up and glows if there is electricity flowing to it. A glass bulb surrounds the filament. It keeps the filament safe from air. Fen makes sure that her light bulb is intact. The filament is in place. The glass is not cracked. It seems to be just fine!

One Last Thing

"I still haven't found the problem yet!" Fen says. She feels like she may never find and fix her problem. Her mom tells her that she has to be **persistent** and think of every possible issue that might arise in a circuit. Are there other things she hasn't checked yet?

Fen realizes that she hasn't checked the switch yet. That's the last thing! The switch controls the flow of electricity through the circuit. If the arm of the switch is up, that means the switch is open. If the switch is open, then the electricity can't flow through it. If the arm of the switch is down, that means the switch is closed. Electricity can flow through it. Fen checks the switch. It is open!

Fen Finds the Problem!

Fen found the source of her problem. The arm of the switch is open. No wonder her light bulb didn't light up! The electricity couldn't get to the light bulb because the open switch disrupted the path of the current.

"I found the problem!" Fen tells her mom. Her mom says she's not done yet. Now, she needs to examine her problem and think of possible solutions. "There are many solutions that you can **implement** in any given situation, but you must check them first," Fen's mom says. Fen thinks about all that she learned about circuits and their parts. How can she fix the switch and make electricity flow throughout the whole circuit?

Fen's Solution

All of the sudden, Fen gets an idea. It's as if a light bulb has turned on in her own head! If the switch is closed, then the electricity will be able to flow again and connect the parts. Now, Fen needs to try out her solution to see if it works.

Fen closes the arm of the switch. The light bulb lights up! She found the problem *and* fixed it. Her mom is very proud of her for not giving up on her circuit kit. Fen has learned to keep going when she finds a problem. She can learn as much as possible about something before trying to find a solution. "Maybe I'll be an electrical engineer someday!" Fen tells her mom.

Glossary

chemical reaction: A chemical change that happens when two or more things combine to form a new thing.

conductor: Matter through which electricity flows easily.

container: An object used to hold something.

current: A flow of electricity resulting from the movement of particles such as electrons.

diagram: A chart, graph, or drawing that shows facts.

disrupt: To interrupt the normal course of something.

engineer: Someone who plans and builds machines.

implement: To carry out.

insulate: To prevent the transfer of electricity.

material: Something from which something else can be made.

persistent: Continuing to do something despite challenges.

research: Studying to find something new.

transform: To change into something else.

Index

C
chemical reaction, 13
conductor, 14
container, 13
copper, 14
current, 7, 20

D
device, 5, 8, 9, 13
diagram, 17
disrupt, 7, 20

E
engineer, 4, 22

I
implement, 20
insulate, 14

M
material, 14

P
parallel, 7
pathway, 8, 9
persistent, 19
power source, 5, 8, 9, 13

R
research, 13

S
series, 7
switch, 5, 8, 9, 10, 19, 20, 22

T
transform, 13